toploader

onka's big moka

toploader

joseph washbourn
voice, piano, organ

julian deane
lead guitar, backing vocals

dan hipgrave
rhythm and acoustic guitar

matt knight
bass guitar

rob green
drums, percussion

When I was about ten, someone gave me the songbook of Elton John's "Greatest Hits". This, and subsequent books, changed the way I saw music completely. Rather than try to play the music of the long dead classical composers, I could now play the songs I'd heard on the radio.

This is the first time our music has <u>ever</u> been written down and it makes me very happy to think that you may get as much enjoyment out of playing our music as we did writing it .

Love Joseph .

exclusive distributors:
music sales limited
8/9 frith street, london w1d 3jb, england.
music sales pty limited
120 rothschild avenue, rosebery, nsw 2018, australia.

order no.am968253
isbn 0-7119-8585-5

music arranged by derek jones.
music engraved by paul ewers music design.

printed in the united kingdom by caligraving limited, thetford, norfolk.

WISE PUBLICATIONS

Let The People Know

Words & Music by Joseph Washbourn

A
Dm7
G
heart, but ba-by it's time to make a brand new
A
Dm7
G
A
start. Life's ev - er-chang-ing in your eyes, but the
Dm9
fr3
F/C
Bm7add11
E
E aug
time for re-ar-rang - ing will a-rise.
Dm7
G
C6
F
Through the rain and snow let the peo - ple know,

Dm7
G
A7sus4
A7
Dm7
G
let the peo - ple know the way.
And when it's time to go
C
F
Bm7add11
E7
Am
let the peo - ple show,
let the peo - ple show the way.
1.
D9
Am
D9
fr4
(Ah)
2.
Am
D9
Am
If the peo-ple want to know,

D9
fr4
Am
D9
fr4
show them the way.
If the peo-ple got to know,
show them the way.
3
A
Dm7
G
3. Fly-ing high,
you left be-hind the sha-dows in your
A
Dm7
G
A
mind.
The sun came out and put them out of time.
The
Dm7
G
A
rhy-thm you can feel's in time with mine.
Hey! So

Dm7
G
A
come on ba - by let's go for a ride, yeah. And
Dm7
G
A
life still keeps on chang - ing in your eyes. But
Dm9
fr3
F/C
Bm7add11
E
chan - ges come and go and so do I.
Dm7
G
C6
F
Through the rain and snow let the peo - ple know,

Verse 2:
Living high, pushing back the boundaries with a smile
Effortless but only for a while
A deity comes to you in the night
Lightens up your day without a fight
And life's still everchanging in your eyes
But the time for rearranging will arise.

Through the rain and snow *etc.*

Dancing In The Moonlight

Words & Music by Sherman Kelly

Fm7
B♭
E♭
fr3
it's a su - per - na - tu - ral de-light. Ev - 'ry - bo - dy's danc-
B♭/D
Cm
Cm/B♭
Fm9
B♭
- ing in the moon - light.
E♭
B♭/D
Cm
Cm/B♭
2. Ev - 'ry - bo - dy here
Fm7
B♭
E♭
B♭/D
Cm
is out of sight. They don't bark and they don't bite.
(Verse 3 see block lyric)

Cm/B♭
Fm7
B♭
E♭
fr3
They keep things loose, they keep it tight. Ev - 'ry - bo - dy's danc-
B♭/D
Cm
Cm/B♭
- ing in the moon - light. Danc -
Fm9
B♭
E♭
B♭/D
Cm
- ing in the moon - light. Ev - 'ry - bo - dy's feel - ing warm and bright,
Cm/B♭
Fm9
B♭
E♭
it's such a fine and na - tural sight. Ev - 'ry - bo - dy's danc-

1.
B♭/D
Cm
Cm/B♭
Fm9
B♭
-ing in the moon-light.
E♭
B♭/D
Cm
3. We like our fun
2.
Fm7
Bsus2
B♭
E♭
B♭/D
Cm
B♭
Organ
Fm7
B♭
E♭
B♭/D
Cm
Cm/B♭
We get it on

Fm7
B♭
most ev - 'ry night and when that moon
E♭
B♭/D
Cm
Cm/B♭
Fm9
B♭
is big and bright it's a su - per - na - tu - ral de - light.
E♭
B♭/D
Cm
Cm/B♭
Ev - 'ry - bo - dy's danc - ing in the moon - light. Danc -
Fm9
B♭
E♭
- ing in the moon - light. Ev - 'ry - bo - dy's feel -
fr3

Verse 3:
We like our fun and we never fight
You can't dance and stay uptight
It's a supernatural delight
Everybody was dancing in the moonlight.

Dancing in the moonlight *etc.*

Breathe

Words & Music by Joseph Washbourn

G
F
nev - er did breathe out.
G
Gmaj9
G9
fr4
G6/9
This tale re - minds me of you, though a dif-f'rent shade of blue. You can-not
Cm7/G
G
al-ways take and nev-er give, this is not how to live. You got-ta
F/G
C/G
G
breathe in and out. You got - ta

1.
F/G
C/G
G
Gmaj9
spread a lit - tle love all a - round.
G9
G6/9
Cm7/G
Am7(♭5)
fr4
fr3
2,3.
G
F/G
C/G
You got - ta breath in and out.
G
F/G
C/G
To Coda
You got - ta spread a lit - tle love all a - round,

G
Dm
Dm/C
Bm7(♭5)
B♭dim7
now. Yeah, I feel in you a - no - ther
Dm/A
G
Dm/F
A7/E
Dm
Dm/C
way to be. Yeah, yeah, yeah. Yeah, I watch as you
Bm7(♭5)
B♭dim7
Dm/A
G
Dm/F
A7/E
breathe ov - er me, yeah, yeah I'm
B♭maj7
F
breath - ing.

B♭maj7
F
C
D.%. al Coda
Coda
G
Yeah, ba - by now.
F
C
(Breathe in and out.
G
) You got - ta breathe in and out.
3
F
C
(Spread a lit - tle love all a - round.
G
) You got - ta breathe in and out.
F
C
(Ooh in and out.

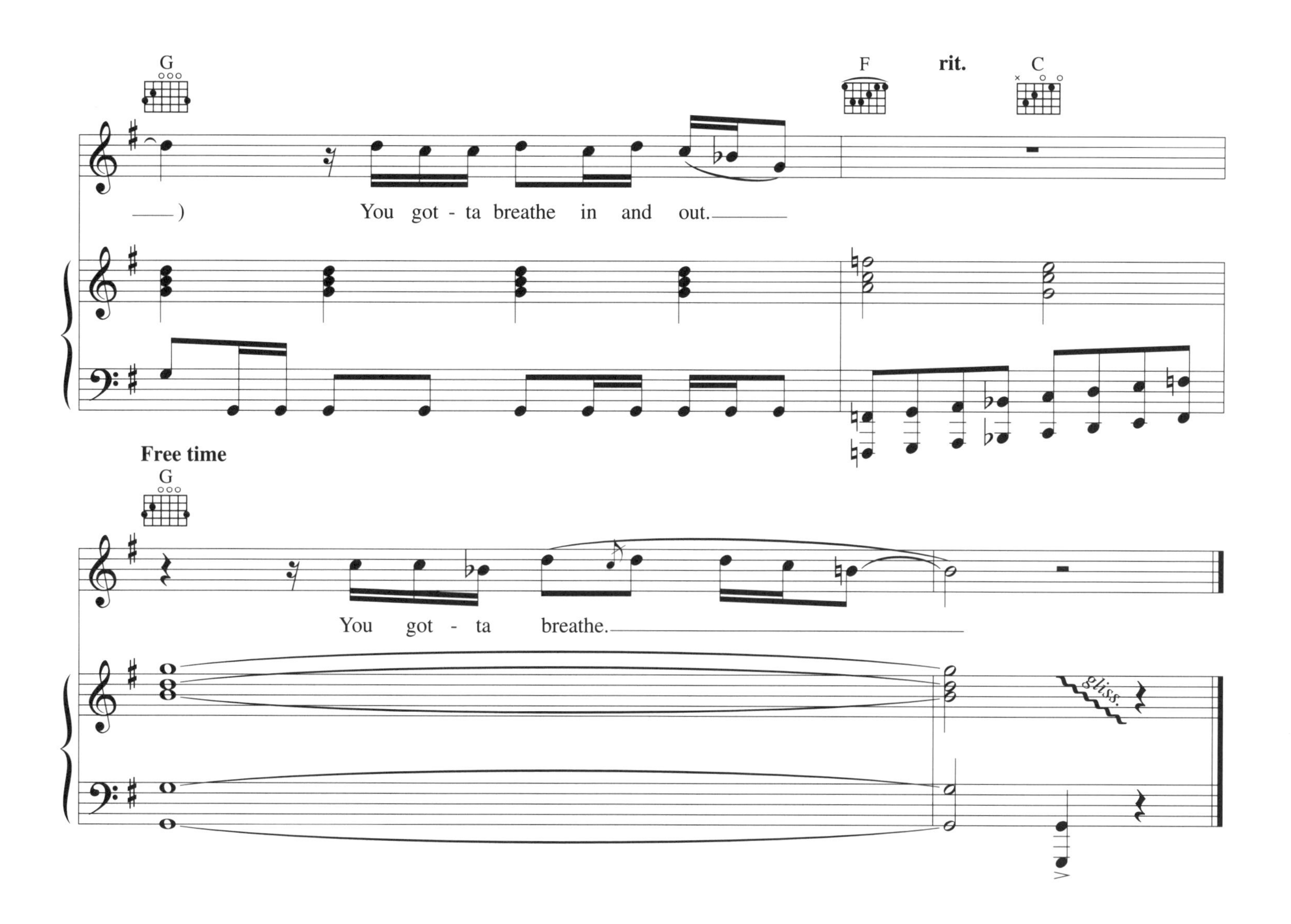

Verse 2:
Though I don't know this for sure
Just another knock at my door
A sprinkling of an inkling underneath an apple tree
I'll tell you when I find out
And show you what it is to breathe out
A natural progression lesson messing up your mind.

You gotta breathe in and out *etc.*

Verse 3:
Like a tale on Jackanory
The end to this unusual story
Is a breath upon a window pane, so come on
Step out of the rain.

Though I'd like to think this were true
You've become a deeper shade of blue
In my eyes, this comes as no surprise
You've nothing left to give… no.

You gotta breath in and out *etc.*

Achilles Heel

Words & Music by Joseph Washbourn

Fsus4
C7sus4/G
A♭maj7
B♭sus2
feel love flow like a riv - er flow. You and I stand - ing still. You are my A -
A♭maj7
B♭sus2
C5
E♭6
- chil - les heel. Ooh, ooh, ooh, ooh, ooh, ooh,
Fsus4
C sus4/G
A♭maj7
B♭sus2
A♭maj7
B♭sus2
ooh, ooh, ooh, ooh.
C5
E♭6
Fsus4
C7sus4/G
2. Feel - ing free, yeah, what a - bout me? Well you got - ta give it up cos I feel love. Do you know

A♭maj7
B♭sus2
how I feel? You are my A - chil - les heel.
C5
E♭6
Fsus4
C7sus4/G
Good - bye to the sky, I know I can't fly but I feel love. Do you know
how I feel? You are my A - chil - les heel. For there's a child in your eyes and the
F
E♭add9
B♭sus4
B♭5
F/A
child nev - er dies. So keep the dream a - live. (Ooh) With the

E♭6
B♭
F
To Coda
aid of sec-ond sight I can push with all my might to make a sta-tue in the sky
Cm/E♭
G/B
C5
E♭6
of my A-chil-les heel. Ooh, ooh, ooh, ooh, ooh, ooh,
Fsus4
Csus4/G
A♭maj7
B♭sus2
A♭maj7
B♭sus2
ooh, ooh, ooh, ooh.
C5
E♭6
Fsus4
C7sus4/G
3. Small fry, don't know why I got-ta get high just to love life. You are my

A♭maj7
B♭sus2
A♭maj7
B♭sus2
C5
E♭6
highs and lows from my head to my toes. I said hey la, will I go far?
Fsus4
C7sus4/G
A♭maj7
B♭sus2
Will I go far cos I love life. Do you know how I feel? You are my A-
A♭maj7
B♭sus2
C5
E♭6
-chil - les heel. I said oh, no, no, will I go slow?
D.%. al Coda
Fsus4
C7sus4/G
A♭maj7
B♭sus2
A♭maj7
B♭sus2
Will I go slow when the feel-ing flows feel-ing flows. For there's a

Coda
E♭
fr3
C5
Cm7
Of my A - chil - les heel.
F sus4/C
C7sus4
A♭maj7/C
B♭sus2/D
Of my A - chil - les heel.
A♭maj7/C
B♭sus2/D
C5
E♭6
Of my A - chil - les heel. Ooh, ooh, ooh, ooh, ooh, ooh,
Fsus4
C sus4/G
A♭maj7
B♭sus2
A♭maj7
B♭sus2
ooh, ooh, ooh, ooh.
Well you're

Outro:

2º I said hello and goodbye but I don't know why.
Well, while we're small fry, on the line.

3º With my Achilles heel, Achilles heel.

Only For A While

Words & Music by Joseph Washbourn

B♭
B♭maj7sus4
E♭
F7
B♭
the line it came true and all a - round.
E♭
F add11
E♭
F add11
2. In - side dreams it stays dor - mant through these
(Verse 3 see block lyric)
E♭
F7
B♭
E♭
F
days that fol - low,
re-mind - ed on - ly by
E♭
F
E♭
F/A
B♭
Fm6/A♭
the sad - dest lul - la - by that was whis - pered.

G7sus4
G
Cm
F
You've got to lie down for a - while,
this will pass,
B♭
E♭maj7
E♭
1.
A♭
Cm
it's on - ly mild.
You've got to ease your mind
D aug
G
for a while.
2. A♭
A♭maj7
Cm
ease your mind,
you've got to

A♭
Cm
ease your mind for a while,
F
F7
rit.
yeah, yeah.
a tempo
Cm
F
B♭
Lie down for a while, this will pass, it's on - ly mild.
E♭maj7
E♭
A♭
Cm
D aug
You've got to ease your mind for a while.

Verse 3:
I know I'll never be able to be free
From these memories
Have love in life the same
Embrace it every day
That it comes to you

You've got to lie down for a while *etc.*

Do You Know What Your Future Will Be?

Words & Music by Joseph Washbourn

F
F♯
G
Thank the hea - vens a - bove these days are gone,
C
G
yeah, yeah, yeah, yeah, yeah, yeah. 2. Keep good faith on the shelf,
(Verse 4 see block lyric)
Am7
F
use it when you're not well, yeah, yeah, all the mis-takes that you made,
F♯
G
don't mat-ter now, no. Do you

C
B♭6/9
know what your fu - ture will be?
8va
A7
A
C
Do you know what your fu - ture will be?
(8va)
B♭6/9
A7
1.
To Coda
A
(8va)
3
2.
A7
D
Yeah, yeah, yeah, yeah.
8va

E♭
fr3
B♭
Get up, get down, run - ning a - round the town.
8va
Round and round in your head, you got-ta rest your sleep - y head,
(8va)
D
D7
G
yeah, yeah.
5. So when you look to the past,
Am7
F
you won't miss what you're miss - ing yeah, yeah, yeah, thank the hea-vens a - bove

G
D.%. al Coda
these days are gone.
Do you
Coda
C
Do you know what your fu - ture will bring?
8va
B♭6/9
A
A7
Play 4 times ad lib.
Do you
(8va)
3
C
B♭6/9
know what your fu - ture, your fu - ture, your fu - ture, your fu -
8va

Verse 3:
Don't wear your heart on your sleeve
Too many lives to retrieve
Mother nature will help you if you let her.

Verse 4:
Keep back a bit for yourself
Keep it with faith on the shelf
Safe under your wing it's just a silly thing.

Do you know *etc.*

Just Hold On

Words & Music by Dave Smith, Tim Woodcock & Mike Terry

C9
D
now it's on - ly get - ting you down.
D
2. I miss the sun - shine that was a good friend of mine, can't stand it as my life goes by.
(Verse 3 see block lyric)
G
C9
Wait - ing for some - thing but no - thing's gon - na hap - pen to - night.
D
Em7
Walk - ing down a one - way road,

D/F♯
Gmaj7
A
but you still don't know which way to turn. Just hold on,
D
D/F♯
G
E7/G♯
just hold on. When you're feel-
D
Bm7
Em7
1. C
-ing like you can't go on, just hold on, just hold on.
D
2. C
3. Rid-ing

B♭
C
F
C/E
Dm
C
When you think you can't make it, just hold on, just hold on,
B♭
G
A
just hold on, just hold on. Ooh!
D
D/F♯
G
E7/G♯
When you're feel-
D
Bm7
Em7
C
- ing like you can't go on, just hold on, just hold on,

Verse 2:
Riding life's rollercoaster
You're making the most of what you can
And what you can't have
Hoping for someone
To show you to another path
Walking down a one-way road
But you still don't know which way to turn.

Just hold on *etc.*

High Flying Bird

Words & Music by Joseph Washbourn

C/G
G
Gm7
fr3
from the earth.
He sees as he flies and
knows as he sees the mas - ses be - low, there's
trou - ble be - low.
1.
2, 3.
2. This

C/G
G
Gm7
fr3
C/G
G
Oh, this white bird flies
yeah, yeah, yeah.
C6
B♭maj7
F
I feel you in my sleep when the sun's down and the
E♭
fr3
C7
B♭maj7
world sleeps be - low, you call a - cross end - less o - ceans,
To Coda
F
E♭
fr3
G
Gm7
fr3
I hear you and want to fly too.

C
G
Gm7
fr3
C
G
D.%. al Coda
3. There's
Coda
C6
B♭maj7
I feel you in my sleep when the
F
E♭
fr3
C9
sun's down and the world sleeps be - low, you call a - cross
B♭maj7
F
E♭6
end - less o - ceans, I hear you and want to fly too.

Verse 2:
This high flying bird has no sense of time
For a thousand years he's climbed these skies
His brothers have burned
Flown too close to the sun
But higher and higher
This white bird flies
This white bird flies.

I feel you in my sleep *etc.*

Verse 3:
There's no turning back as blue becomes black
The air becomes thin, this flight begins
But the bird can still breathe
Brighter that before
On celestial wing
This bird can now sing
This bird can now sing.

I feel you in my sleep *etc.*

Higher State

Words & Music by Joseph Washbourn

C
F7
B♭
1. There is no time to be low, to-mor-row there's on-ly time to kill.
E♭
G7/D
C
F7
There is no time to be high and fly,
B♭
G7
G7(♯9)
fr3
there's on-ly time to thrill. So when
C
F
D7
G
I am up and you are down ba-by, that's when you got-ta come a-round. Got-ta

C
F
D7
G
ease my pain and soothe my brain, got-ta take me in out of this rain.
C
F
D7
F
Some-thing's on so don't be late, it's time to leave for the high-er state.
C
F
B♭
2. There is no rhyme to ex-press my e-mo-tion, there's on-ly rhyme to feel.
(Verse 3 see block lyric)
E♭
fr3
G7/D
fr2
C
And there is no rhyme to ful-

F9
B♭
E♭
fr3
-fill my de-vo-tion, there's on-ly rhyme to heal.
A♭
fr4
E♭/G
(Don't fret, get high, there's a new dawn that says hi.)
The high - er state,
yeah.
(Don't fret, get high, there's a new dawn that says hi.)
The high - er state,
To Coda
yeah.
(Don't fret, get high, there's a new dawn that says hi.)
The high - er state,

A♭
E♭/G
C
F
D7
G7
fr4
fr3
Guitar
yeah,
yeah.
(Don't fret, get high.)
C
F
D7
G7
C
G
It's a hap-py day for you and I, the sun
D7
G7
C
F
is up shin-ing in the sky, got a heart of gold that I can see ba-by,
D7
F
you got you, now you got me.
gliss.

Verse 3:
It is no crime to be lost with no direction
It's just a crime not to live
And there is no crime to be asked for affection
It's just a crime not to live.

Don't fret, get high *etc.*

Summer Cycle

Words & Music by Joseph Washbourn

Gm9
C/G
fr3
Synth.
1. The
sun, it kiss my cheek, yeah that feels fine. The
(Verse 2 see block lyric)
breeze, it strokes my feet, yeah that feels fine.
Los - ing the track of the time, con -

Gm9
C/G
Gm9
C/G
Gm9
C/G
Gm9
C/D
-fused in a sun-cov-ered life.
1.
E♭maj7
D7/F♯
Gm9
Gm
Dm7/F
E♭maj7
D7
Gm9
Gm
D7/A
Guitar
E♭maj7
D7/F♯
Gm
E♭maj7
D7
Gm9
C/G
Gm9
C/G
Gm9
C/G
Gm9
C/G
2.
E♭maj7
D7/F♯
2. Bird - You might feel

Gm Am7(♭5) E♭maj7 D7/F♯ Gm
laugh - ter in the sun, but
E♭maj7 D7/F♯ Gm Am7(♭5) E♭maj7 D7
laugh - ter might help us when we're done. Ay,
Gm E♭maj7 D7 Gm
ay, ay, ay. You might feel laugh - ter in the
E♭maj7 D7/F♯ Gm E♭maj7 D7/F♯
sun, but laugh - ter might

Gm
Csus2
D7sus4
save us when we're done.
Gm9
C/G
3. Sil - hou-
-et - ted by the sun, my an-gel comes dressed in
white, a broad wide smile out-shines the sun.

Gm9
C/G
Oh, such a pic - ture is this, my
an - gel she stoops for a kiss.
Guitar
8va
(8va)
1.
2.
Gm/D
But well,
fr3

E♭maj7
D7/F♯
Gm
Dm7/A
E♭maj7
D7
You might feel laugh - ter in the sun,
Gm
E♭maj7
D7
Gm
Dm7/A
but laugh - ter might help us when we're
E♭maj7
D7/F♯
Gm
F/A
E♭maj7
D7/F♯
done. Ay, ay. You might feel
Gm
Dm7/F
E♭maj7
D7
Gm
laugh - ter in the sun, but

Verse 2:
Birdsong is all I hear while I am here
I'm lost but cannot see these things I feel
Circles appear in my mind
Floating through space and through time.

You might feel laughter *etc.*

Floating Away (In The Bath Tub)

Words & Music by Joseph Washbourn

1.
F
A♭7
fr4
G7
C
rub.
o - pen my hands to the moon.
2.
A♭
G7
F
dog that ran off with the spoon
or the cow that jumped ov - er the
C
Caug
C6
moon.
C7
Fm6

C
Em/B
C7/B♭
Do you know what it means to be mm, mm,
F/A
A♭
fr4
float-ing a-way,
float-ing a-way?
Rock feel ♩= 66
G
rit.
F
E♭
fr3
Guitar
D♭
Fm/C
C
B♭
Float-ing a-way,

Verse 2:
Splishing and splashing and wishing and rushing
It's more fun in here than the zoo
Slippery salamanders on my tail
I'm the dog that ran off with the spoon
Or the cow that jumped over the moon.

Just About Living

Words & Music by Joseph Washbourn

F
1. What's ta - boo to you is just not ta - boo to me, do you
(Verse 2 see block lyric)
want to make a deal? There's no-thing I can't steal.
B♭
Yeah, yeah, yeah, yeah,
A♭
fr4
yeah, it's just a - bout
F
liv - ing, so make it

C
A♭/E♭
B♭/E♭
F
strong, make it qui - et a - bout liv - ing,
B♭7/F
To Coda
B♭/E♭
it's just a - bout liv - ing.
A♭
E♭
A♭
B♭7
Life on an I. O. U. but I see hope be - tween us too.
F
A♭
E♭
A♭
Yeah, yeah, yeah. I bor - rowed it from some - one new, some - thing old
fr4
fr3

B♭
1. F
F7/E♭
for some - thing blue it's just a - bout liv - ing.
B♭/D
B♭
A♭6
fr4
B♭
F
2. What means
2. F
-boo to you, ta - boo to me, to you and me, to me and you, get
out that gun now go and give just a - bout now how to live.

Fm7
Guitar
B♭/F
Fm7
N.C.
What's ta - boo — to you — is just not ta - boo — to me, — do you

D.%. al Coda
want to make a deal? There's no-thing I can't steal.
Coda
A♭
fr4
E♭
fr3
B♭
Life on an I. O. U. but I see hope be-tween us too.
F
A♭
E♭
Yeah, yeah, yeah. I bor-rowed it from some-one new, some-thing old
B♭
F
A♭
yeah, some-thing old, there's some - thing blue.

Verse 2:
What means lots and lots to you
May mean nothing much to me
But ask me while I'm here
Or forget it for a year
It's just about living.

So make it strong *etc.*

1/01 (39366)